BEN
BOLD

Ben the Bold sees a bear.
"Grrr!" says Ben the Bold.

Ben the Bold sees a lion.
"Grrr!" says Ben the Bold.

Ben the Bold sees a snake.
"Grrr!" says Ben the Bold.

4

Ben the Bold sees a tiger.
"Grrr!" says Ben the Bold.

5

Ben the Bold sees a dog.
"Grrr!" says Ben the Bold.

Ben the Bold sees a kitten.
"Yelp!" says Ben the Bold.

Ben the Bold runs away!